A Hairy Question

by Hazel Edwards

illustrated by Rae Dale

The Characters

Freya
I get a haircut.

Jan
She thinks
everything is easy.

Mum & **Dad**
They liked
my long hair.

Peter
My brother.

The Setting

SCHOOL

SWIMMING POOL

FREYA'S HOME

CONTENTS

Chapter 1

Haircuts

"Who cut your hair?" said one
of the kids as I walked in
the school gate.

"Have the rats been at your hair?"
said another. "Or is it a bird's
nest?"

I heard Ned say, "Freya, have you
seen Dracula?"

It was Monday morning, the first
school day after my new haircut.
I didn't want to be at school.
I knew what people were saying.

My hair looked terrible.
One side was shorter than the other.
The left side stuck out.
The right side went under.

My friend Jan sat next to me.

"It doesn't look too bad," she said,
as we waited for Mr Marash,
our teacher.

I didn't believe Jan.
My new haircut was all her fault.
Jan had to say it looked good.
On Saturday, she had cut my hair!

CHAPTER  2

Jan and Her Wild Ideas

Jan does some silly things.
Cutting my hair was one of her
wild ideas.

My hair was very long. It was black and straight. It was so long
I could sit on it. I mostly wore it tied back in a pony tail.

Jan has short, curly, blonde hair.
I thought it would be great
to have curls like hers.

When we went swimming,
Jan's hair dried fast. Mine took
hours to dry.

Last Friday night we were at the pool.

"I wish my hair was like yours, Jan,"
I said after we got dressed.
"Short hair is so easy to look after."

Jan looked up. She was drying her hair.

"Why don't you get your hair cut, Freya?" she asked. "You could have a perm. That would give you some curls."

I shook my head. The wet ends
of my hair dripped down my back.

"Cut your own hair," said Jan
with a smile. "It's easy."

"I did mine once," she added.
"It looked all right. The hair just
curled up by itself."

As we shut the locker and walked
out of the changing rooms,
I thought about a haircut.

My hair was still dripping down my back. Jan's curls were already dry.

"I bet I could cut your hair," said Jan.

CHAPTER  3

The Home Haircut

I wondered if I should let Jan
cut my hair.

"On Saturday I could cut it.
Then I could do a home perm
for you," Jan offered.

My Mum and Dad would be at work on Saturday. Peter, my little brother would be playing football.

The house would be empty.
So, I made up my mind.

"Okay, let's do it," I said.

That was my mistake. Letting Jan
cut my hair was a stupid idea.

At two o'clock I could sit on my hair.
Then Jan began to cut.
Snip. Snip. Snip.

"I've never had it cut," I told Jan.

I watched Jan cutting my hair
in the bathroom mirror.
Snip. Snip. Snip.

Jan said, "What a lot of hair
you've got."

"Had!" I replied.

The bathroom floor was covered in long black hair.

"Easy," said Jan as she cut. "Piece of cake!"

I remembered when Jan said cooking
was easy. We spent an afternoon
scraping burnt food off the stove.

Jan had also told me that camping was easy. The tent fell on top of us during the night.

Camping

By three o'clock on Saturday afternoon
there was more hair
on the bathroom floor
than on my head.

Ten years of hair was on the floor.
I wanted it back, but it was
too late!

"Look in the mirror," said Jan.

I did. There was a lot of face and not much hair.

"Is it all right?" Jan said, looking worried.

What could I say? It was too late.

"One side is longer than the other,"
I said softly.

Jan cut some more.
"Do you want a fringe?" she asked.

"All right," I said.

Jan cut some more. Snip. Snip. Snip.

"Have a look," said Jan.

In the mirror, I looked strange.
My long hair had gone.
Bits of short hair
stuck out everywhere.

Jan's face was white.

"Shampoo it, then it will look better.
Short hair dries fast," Jan said,
as she swept my ex-hair
into a dustpan.

It did dry fast. But wisps of hair still stuck out.

"It will look better with curls,"
said Jan, putting my old hair
into the kitchen bin.
"Now for the perm."

CHAPTER 4

That Terrible Haircut

"Here's the packet," said Jan. "Perms are easy. I bought some special rollers."

I shuddered.

What should I do? Could a perm
be worse? ... What would
Dad say?

"No thanks, Jan. It might be worse."

"It looks all right," said Jan.
"It's just different."

She was being kind. It looked
terrible.

At five o'clock Mum, Dad and Peter
came home. My hair was in rollers.
None of them could tell how short
it was.

"Put the rubbish out please, Peter," said Mum.

"There's a pile of hair in here," Peter yelled.

"Shhh!"

CHAPTER 5

What They Said

"Freya has cut her hair off!" yelled Peter.

"Just act as if you've come up with a new fashion," she said.

I smiled.

"Let's make new clothes to wear with your new hair," said Jan. "It's easy to sew. I'll show you how to follow a pattern."

"No thanks, Jan. Let's go swimming instead. My hair will dry quickly now. That's one good thing."

Jan smiled. "But it is easy to sew."

I smiled back. "No thanks. I want to go swimming."

In about ten years, my hair
will be long again. I might as well
swim a lot while it's short.

GLOSSARY

different
not the same

dracula
a scary monster

fault
a mistake

offer
wanting to do or
give something nice

pattern
a flat plan to make
a model or clothing

perm
makes hair go curly
(short for permanent wave)

piece of cake
simple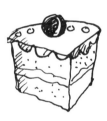

shuddered
to shake from fear
or horror

terrible
very bad, awful

Hazel Edwards

Hazel Edwards' hair changes sometimes. As an author of over 130 books, Hazel uses "participant-observer" research as an excuse for doing unusual things like hot air ballooning or belly-dancing. *There's a Hippopotamus on Our Roof Eating Cake,* her best known book, is 21 this year.
Visit www.newwebcity.com/hazel/edwards.htm

Rae Dale

Rae Dale was born in Melbourne, Australia. After obtaining her Diploma of Advertising Art, she taught in various schools. Now painting and illustrating are her major interests, as well as reading, gardening, washing dishes and collecting proverbs.